SMETANA.

Bartered
bride.

782.1.

SMETANA
Bartered bride.

004

This book is due for return on or before the last date shown
above but it may be renewed by personal application, post,
or telephone, quoting this date and details of the book

 Northamptonshire Libraries

To
Dr. THOMAS GARRIGUE MASARYK
President of the Czechoslovak Republic
this English version is respectfully dedicated

THE
BARTERED BRIDE
Comic Opera
in Three Acts

◉

Libretto by
KARL SABINA

English version (from the Czech) by
ROSA NEWMARCH

Music by
FREDERIC SMETANA

Hawkes & Son (London) Ltd.

Sole Selling Agents : Boosey & Hawkes, Ltd.
London · Paris · Bonn · Capetown · Sydney · Toronto · Buenos Aires · New York

CHARACTERS

KRUŠINA* -	a peasant - - -	Baritone
LUDMILA -	his wife - - -	Soprano
MAŘENKA -	their daughter - -	Soprano
MICHA -	a peasant - - -	Bass
HATA -	his second wife -	Mezzo-Soprano
VAŠEK* -	her son - - -	Tenor
JENIK -	son of Micha's first wife -	Tenor
KECAL* -	the village marriage broker -	Bass
THE MANAGER	of a company of strolling players	Tenor
ESMERALDA -	a dancer - - -	Soprano
THE INDIAN -	a member of the company -	Tenor

Villages, actors, children

*Pronounced : Krushina ; Vashek ; Ketsal

The scene is laid in a Bohemian village on the afternoon and evening of the Patron Saint's Day. The action takes place during the first half of the nineteenth century.

INDEX

IMPORTANT NOTICE—To simplify the production of this Opera the recitative work may be performed as dialogue.

THE BARTERED BRIDE

Overture

Words by
KAREL SABINA
English Version by
ROSA NEWMARCH

Music by
F. SMETANA

Printed in England

H. 14079

The Bartered Bride

The Bartered Bride

H. 14079

4

The Bartered Bride

The Bartered Bride

6

The Bartered Bride

H. 14079

The Bartered Bride

H. 14079

8

H. 14079

The Bartered Bride

The Bartered Bride

The Bartered Bride

The Bartered Bride

H. 14079

The Bartered Bride

H. 14079

14

ACT I
Scene 1

Mařenka, Jeník, Village folk

The village green. On one hand the **inn**. On the other a fair is being held.

The Bartered Bride

H. 14079

The Bartered Bride

16

The Bartered Bride

18

The Bartered Bride

H. 14079

The Bartered Bride

H. 14079

22

The Bartered Bride

H. 14079

The Bartered Bride

H. 14079

-ly, ne-ver giv-ing way, firm-ly keep to what.......... you

Tempo I

say!

p CHORUS

Cease your sigh - ing, cease your sigh - ing, leave off cry - ing,...........

Tempo I

cresc.

.... For you know that true love ne - ver Runs an

cresc.

cresc.

The Bartered Bride   H. 14079

The Bartered Bride

The Bartered Bride

Since God gives us health to-day, health to-day, Since God gives us health to-day....

ff Più mosso

.... On - ly they are real - ly hap - py, Who en - joy life

Più mosso

while they may, while they may, On - ly they are real - ly hap - py, Who en -

The Bartered Bride

H. 14079

leggiero

join the danc-ing fol-low, fol-low, like the **Ko-lo**, Come, come! We hear the

fol-low fol-low, There's no so-lace

fid-dles' sound, Join the round, join the **round!** We hear the fid-dles'sound,

Join the round, join the round! We hear the fid-dles' sound, Join the round,

dim.

dim. sempre   *dim.*

dim.

The Bartered Bride

H. 14079

Scene 2
Mařenka and Jeník

The Bartered Bride

H. 14079

ask that! how could I be-long to a-ny o-ther man but you, be-lov-ed? But my

par - ents! Fa - ther pledg'd his hon - our! That was a

JENÍK

MAŘENKA

pi - ty! You don't seem much con cern'd a-bout it; quite in-dif-fer-ent. Are you not at

all a-larm'd Ra-ther pleas'd per-haps! Be - lov - ed, swear to me you have no

o - ther sweetheart, no-one left at home? Ah, is it true I'm not your on-ly

The Bartered Bride

H.14079

love? That you are pi-ning for a-no-ther girl? Ne-ver, ne-ver!

JENÍK

ARIA
Moderato

dolce.

MAŘENKA
Con anima

If I thought you would be faith-less, If I dreamt you could de-ceive,

Ah, if I thought you could de-ceive, Then some un-re-lent-ing

ven-geance for such sin I might con-ceive, for such sin I

The Bartered Bride

H. 14079

might con-ceive, then some un-re-lent-ing ven-geance for such sin I

might con-ceive, for........ such sin I might con-ceive, for........ such sin I might con-

-ceive.

Then con-fess to me,........ my Je-ník what in-just-ice had wound-ed

you, That you left your home and pa-rents and per-chance a sweetheart

The Bartered Bride

The Bartered Bride

                                                                                          H.14079

pack-ing! So out in-to the world I went, And

Allegro

found a way to earn my bread Among strangers!

DUET
Andante ♩= 52

JENÍK

Tho' a moth - er is a bless - ing,

A cru - el step mother's noth - - - ing but a curse.

Should she hate a poor shy, de-fence-less or-phan lad,

MAŘENKA

She'd grow more spite - ful, And she'd treat him worse and worse.

Aye, a moth - er is a bless - ing, But a step -
Tho' a moth - er is a bless - ing,   A cru - el

- moth - - er is a curse.   Should she dis -
step-moth-er's noth - - ing but a curse.   Should she dis - like

- like a poor......... de - fence - less or-phan lad, She'd treat him worse,
Should she dis - like   an   or-phan lad, She'd treat him worse,

The Bartered Bride

The Bartered Bride

44

The Bartered Bride

H. 14079

The Bartered Bride

H. 14079

The Bartered Bride

The Bartered Bride

H. 14079

48

come! ... And my fa - ther is with them,

Più mosso

they search for me.
sotto voce
I would ra-ther not be seen. Tempo I.

più f

Fare - - - well, ... fare - - - well,
dolce ... cresc.

Fare - - - well,
f
dear - - - est mai-den mine! Think of me when I'm
p dolce

H. 14079

The Bartered Bride

Scene 3

Ludmila, Krušina, Kecal

KECAL

As I said be-fore, old cro-ny; you, you you have giv'n your word,

now you must keep stea-dy-O and stick to what you pro-mis'd.

Now all is rea-dy-O, now all is rea-dy-O, now

all is rea-dy-O, So you must still keep firm and steady now for all is rea-dy-O!

If

in me you will be-lieve, You'll quick-ly sign and seal, I'm shrewd as

you can see, But a has-ty glance will not re-veal How cle-ver I can

The Bartered Bride

The Bartered Bride

H. 14079

54

The Bartered Bride

H. 14079

The Bartered Bride

H. 14079

56

The Bartered Bride

59

The Bartered Bride   H.14079

60

The Bartered Bride

H. 14079

Recitative

you would give your daugh - - ter To wed his son!

LUDMILA

Then tell us now, which of Mi - cha's sons Is for our daugh-ter?

KECAL

Do you ask? Why, of course there is on - ly

one— Va - šek! Je - ník, Mi - cha's first born, is a

bad lot, And no one knows where he has gone!

63

The Bartered Bride

H. 14079

For his be - ha - - viour's so gen - tle, He is like a per - fect

lamb. Vi - - ces he has none; An - y mo - ther might be

Proud to own a son So no - ble as our Va - šek. I'm quite sure of that, — I

am! Such..... a nice lad, So well - train'd and god - ly; What mat - ter

if he speaks A tri - fle slow and odd - ly? For his be-

The Bartered Bride

H.14079

The Bartered Bride

The Bartered Bride

70

The Bartered Bride

H. 14079

Scene 4

The same people and Mařenka

KECAL

me you're seek - - ing? You'll re-joice to hear of what we're speak - - ing!

Don't you want a sweet-heart, One to play a lo-ver's part?

I've the ve-ry man for you, Well - off, good and hand - some too.

MAŘENKA

Well - off and good, *and* hand-some too?

KRUŠINA
f risoluto

When this

swain you see, You will be con - tent.

The Bartered Bride

H. 14079

 H. 14079

74

The Bartered Bride

H. 14079

The Bartered Bride

76

The Bartered Bride

H. 14079

The Bartered Bride

The Bartered Bride

H. 14079

H. 14079

The Bartered Bride.

RECITATIVE

MAŘENKA

I'll not part from my man, so there! Be-lieve me, you may be quite sure of that!

KRUŠINA

Keep him, or send him pack-ing, girl. 'Tis too late to al - ter things,

a tempo

For I gave my bond long a-go to Mi - cha, Sign'd and wit - ness'd.

LUDMILA

Please to tell me, my dear man, What kind of

The Bartered Bride

The Bartered Bride

The Bartered Bride

H. 14079

Scene 5
Finale

The Inn. The elders sit at tables. The young ones prepare to dance.

The Bartered Bride

H.14079

The Bartered Bride

The Bartered Bride

The Bartered Bride

The Bartered Bride

Bas- ses rum-bling, cym-bals chink-ing, Rings of dan-cers in-ter-link-ing,

earth spins round us like a mill, and.............. our feet will

not keep still!..............

The Bartered Bride

End of Act I

H.14079

ACT II
Scene 1
Interior of the Inn.

On one side Jenik and village youths seated at tables drinking beer. On the other side Kecal.

95

The Bartered Bride

H.14079

The Bartered Bride

The Bartered Bride

KECAL

Well, if my ad-vice you ask, I says old Kec-al Who sits there a-part? would not coun-sel greed, But I tell you, dear young peo-ple, That a pock-et full of mon-ey Is the great-est thing in life. Cash out-lasts a moon of hon-ey, So

H. 14079

100

The Bartered Bride

H. 14079

The Bartered Bride

H. 14079

102

The Bartered Bride

H. 14079

Furiant

104

The Bartered Bride

H. 14079

Più mosso

The Bartered Bride

Scene 2

Vašek

The Bartered Bride

H. 14079

Scene 3

Mařenka, Vašek

When she has me?   You? (ha, ha!)   You have not heard?... Have you seen her?

MAŘENKA

VAŠEK

Ne - ne - ne - n - no   On - ly I'm told   that I'm t - t - to be her

MAŘENKA

hus-band!   We know it   too,   and that is why we grieve for you;

You will be de-ceiv'd and suf-fer sore - ly; A - las to die so

VAŠEK

ear - ly! B-b-but that's dreadful!   And y - y - y - y - yet my m-m-m-m-mammy told me

     H. 14079

The Bartered Bride

H. 14079

The Bartered Bride

114

The Bartered Bride

.14079

The Bartered Bride

H. 14079

116

The Bartered Bride

H. 14079

The Bartered Bride

H. 14079

118

The Bartered Bride

H. 14079

120

The Bartered Bride

H. 14079

The Bartered Bride

The Bartered Bride

Scene 4

(Jeník and Kecal)

Recitative

KECAL

I tell you, she's pretty, well-off, Suit-a-ble, and her name is

JENÍK

Li-ly! Oh well, but who knows if she'll ap-prove of me? That is my af-

KECAL

JENÍK

-fair. But you must now re-lin-quish Ma-řen-ka! No, I could not! At the thought my

KECAL

heart would break. He is fit for an a-sy-lum!

Moderato

The chief point is her mon-ey!

124

The Bartered Bride

H. 14079

said that in truth You're but a poor worth-y youth, quite a stea dy wor-ker

too; but with mar - riage, as with love,'tis on-ly cash will do.

Do you pos-ess a pen - ny?

JENÍK

Can one mar-ry and be

hap - py if the purse is light? Pret - ty girls with pau - per

lads their pro-mise will not plight.

KECAL

Quite so!

that's my point of view! I know the world and life! Minus cash, Minus

cash, Minus cash, the mar - riage state is a nest, Of

bick - er - ing and strife, of bick - er - ing and strife....................

.... and strife!

Be so good as to say why round here you're staying;

The Bartered Bride

128

The Bartered Bride

H. 14079

The Bartered Bride

130

The Bartered Bride

H. 14079

131

The Bartered Bride

H. 14079

The Bartered Bride

134

house and gar-den Left her by a wealth - y dad.

KECAL *mf leggiero*

She's cows in plen - ty Sheep a-bout twen - ty, Geese and some gan - ders,

Hens, all good sit - ters, Pigs with such lit - ters, And a dow - ry chest, A dow - ry

chest, a dow - ry chest! An or-chard-field, With trees that yield, And stores of lin - en of the

JENÍK

She's cows in plen - ty Sheep a-bout twen - ty, Geese and some

best. She's cows in plen - ty, Sheep a-bout twen - ty, Geese and some gan - ders,

p leggiero

The Bartered Bride

H. 14079

The Bartered Bride

H. 14079

136

The Bartered Bride

H. 14079

The Bartered Bride

138

The Bartered Bride

Take three hun- dred crowns; if not, Then you can clear out!

JENÍK

Well, we'll call a halt! 'Tis a nice round sum. Plank down the mon- ey, then the

mat- ter's fin- ish'd! — Save for one con - di - tion: that Ma - řen - ka on - ly

ben marcato

con fuoco

mar - ries one spec-ial man, No one else but the son of Mi - cha; Oth- er-

KECAL

-wise, our con-tract sim - ply does not stand. Quite so, quite so, that is un-der-

The Bartered Bride

H. 14079

-stood, ve - ry clear - ly__ That the girl shall mar - ry no one else Than

Mi - cha's son. *JENÍK* And I swear that I'll not part with her To an-oth-er

man than the son of old To-by Mi - cha. And don't for-get to men-tion this!

KECAL Aye, the deed I'll quick - ly write, And keep our wit - ness-es in sight!

JENÍK Yet one more word, Sir__ *KECAL* What? *JENÍK* Add this to what I've said:

The Bartered Bride

Scene 5

The Bartered Bride

146

The Bartered Bride

H. 14079

Scene 6

Jeník, Kecal, Krušina and Villagers

The Bartered Bride

The Bartered Bride

The Bartered Bride

(maliciously)

List-en, there is one thing more of great im-por-tance: Je-nik will re-ceive three hun-dred crowns-three hun-dred,— and for this sum a-grees to sell the bride we thought he lov'd so well!

CHORUS
Oh, how shame-ful, what a black-guard, who will sell his bride for

The Bartered Bride

154

The Bartered Bride   H. 14079

The Bartered Bride

156

KRUŠINA
KECAL

The Bartered Bride

H. 14079

The Bartered Bride

End of Act II

H. 14079

ACT III

Scene 1

The Village green. **Vašek alone and miserable.**

The Bartered Bride

Scene 2

Enter strolling players, villagers and Vašek.

RECITATIVE   MANAGER

Walk up, walk up please, la-dies and gentlemen, we of-fer you   one of the

ve-ry grandest shows   ev-er yet seen in this your fa-mous vil-lage, Such dis-plays of

tight-rope dancing, ac-ro-bat-ics, Dar-ing bareback'd rid-ing, you ne-ver be-held!

162

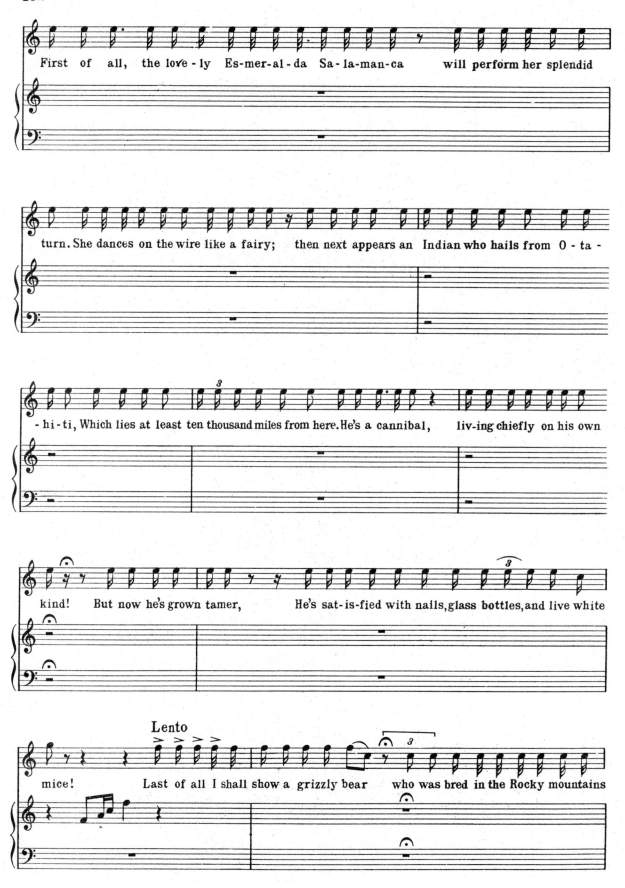

The Bartered Bride

H. 14079

Allegro moderato

Tho' ve - ry sav-age, he dan - ces po-lite-ly with our Span ish la - dy, Miss Es-mer-al-da Sal-a-man-ca in grace - ful, state - ly, An-da-lus-ian dan - ces! Walk up, la - dies and gent-le - men don't fail to see our show! Children un-der three ad-mit-ted half-price. This is tru-ly the grandest sight ev-er seen. Walk up, walk up! Now we start!

The Bartered Bride

The Bartered Bride

H. 14079

The Bartered Bride

The Bartered Bride

H. 14079

168

The Bartered Bride

169

The Bartered Bride

H. 14079

Scene 3

Vašek, the Manager, Esmeralda

The Bartered Bride

172

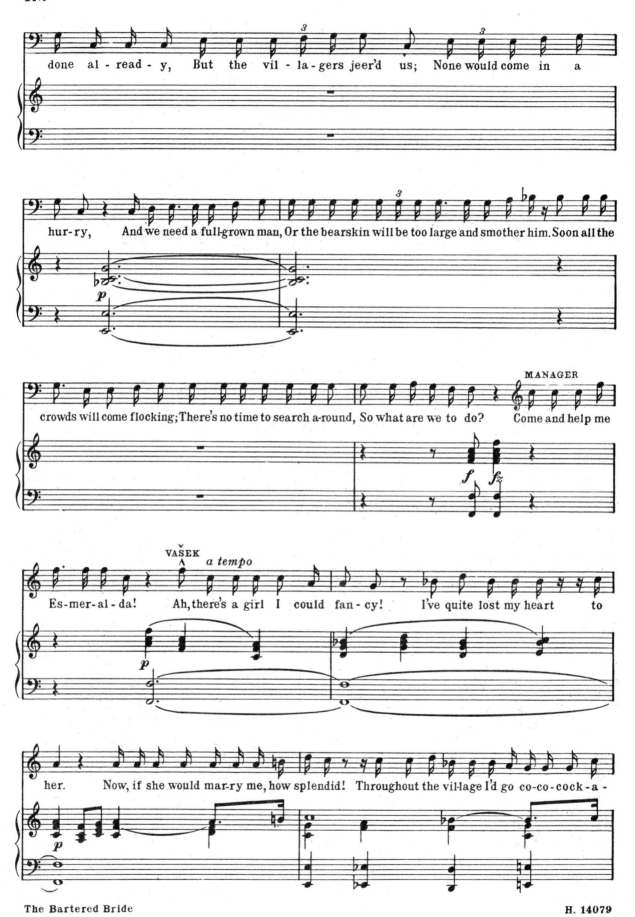

174

VAŠEK
player I can as-sure you, Sir, The rest soon will fol-low. What, me an act-or? I

ESMERALDA
don't know how to act a bit! My............ love will teach you all that you need! Love! That

VAŠEK

Allegro   MANAGER
does sound nice!   Life with us is real-ly jol-ly, Times are quite fair. Mon-ey

a tempo

we can earn in plen-ty, We can wan-der at our fan-cy, And live like birds of air! And,

cresc.

sotto voce

let me say that our fra-ter-ni-ty's re-spect-ed!   Act-ors hold a sta-tus

The Bartered Bride

176

The Bartered Bride

H. 14079

With a gold-en lead. With a bear-ish mask on, You will look so sweet!

lead. *legatissimo*

With a bear-ish

Boots of soft-est leath-er Will set off your feet!

mask on, You will look so sweet!

Boots of soft-est leath-er Will set

dolce p

Like a young A - don - is Proud - ly

off your feet! Like a young A - don - is

you...... will ad - vance, All will cheer you, all ap-

Proud - ly you'll ad-vance, All will cheer you,

The Bartered Bride

Scene 4

Hàta, Kecal, Micha, Vašek

The Bartered Bride

The Bartered Bride

The Bartered Bride

The Bartered Bride

184

The Bartered Bride

H. 11079

The Bartered Bride.

H. 14079

The Bartered Bride

Scene 5

Enter Mařenka in haste with her father and mother

Meno allegro

MAŘENKA

And that's not ve-ry dear!

O shameful deed, O treacher-

Tempo del duetto

How false men's hearts can be!

He swore an oath that life it-self he'd

glad-ly fore-go he'd glad-ly fore-go for me!

KRUŠINA

Calm your-self, my dearest child, for you have nought to rue al-

The Bartered Bride

H. 14079

The Bartered Bride

H. 14079

The Bartered Bride

H. 14079

H. 14079

The Bartered Bride

H. 14039

194

The Bartered Bride

H. 14079

The Bartered Bride

H. 14079

The Bartered Bride

The Bartered Bride

Scene 6

Mařenka

The Bartered Bride

The Bartered Bride

The Bartered Bride

H. 14079

Scene 7

Mařenka Jeník

The Bartered Bride

The Bartered Bride

JENÍK

Now what a stub-born lass you are, Who from the truth is shrink-ing,

Who from the truth is shrink-ing, Al-tho' I thought from your high

looks You'd face it with-out blink-ing! Now what a stub-born lass you are, who

MAŘENKA

Più vivo

With such a faith-less man as you, I'll not dis-cuss or

from the truth is shrink-ing! *Più vivo*

rea - son, I'll not dis-cuss or rea - son, For

dolce.

ne-ver-more I wish to see A wretch so steep'd in trea-son, With such a faith-less

man as you, I'll not dis-cuss or rea-son.

Tempo I

JENÍK
Now what a stub-born lass you are, Who

Tempo I

p

MAŘENKA **Più vivo**
With such a faith-less man as you, I'll

from the truth is shrink-ing.

Più vivo

p leggiero

not dis-cuss or rea-son, I'll not dis-cuss or rea-son, I'll

sf

Meno vivo

not dis-cuss or rea-son! For ne-ver more I wish to

JENÍK

Now what a stub-born lass you are Who

Meno vivo

see a wretch so steep'd in trea-son

from the truth is shrink-ing, Al-tho' I thought from your high looks, you'd

Più vivo

With such a faith-less man as you I'll

face it with-out blink-ing Who

Più vivo

p

Scene 8

Kecal. Mařenka. Jenik.

The Bartered Bride

The Bartered Bride

H. 14079

216

The Bartered Bride

H. 14079

The Bartered Bride

The Bartered Bride

Scene 9

The same. Enter Ludmila, Hata, Micha and Chorus

The Bartered Bride

H. 14079

222

The Bartered Bride

H. 14079

H. 14079

The Bartered Bride

The Bartered Bride

The Bartered Bride

H. 14079

The Bartered Bride

H. 14079

The Bartered Bride

The Bartered Bride

232

The Bartered Bride   H. 14079

The Bartered Bride

The Bartered Bride

The Bartered Bride

Scene 10

H. 14079

238

The Bartered Bride   H. 14079

The Bartered Bride

240

The Bartered Bride

H. 14079

The Bartered Bride

H. 14079

Lowe and Brydone (Printers) Limited, London

VOCAL ALBUMS

* **BOOSEY'S COMMUNITY SONG BOOK.** English, Scotch, Welsh, Irish Songs, Rounds, etc.
* **CLUB SONG BOOK, The.** Separate Editions for Boys and Girls.

ELIZABETHAN LOVE SONGS. Frederick Keel. For high or low voice. Two sets of 60 Songs, arranged with piano accompaniment adapted from the lute tablature.

FIFTY MODERN ENGLISH SONGS. Songs by 20th Century Composers.

GOLDEN TREASURY OF SONG. 83 Songs by Classical Composers in 2 Vols.

HANDEL'S OPERA SONGS. 52 Arias, edited by W. T. Best. Italian-English (R.E.)

HANDEL'S ORATORIO SONGS. 72 Arias edited by W. T. Best (R.E.).

HANDEL'S SONGS. Selected and edited by Walter Ford and R. Erlebach. 7 vols.
    Vol. I : Light Soprano.   Vol. 2 : Dramatic Soprano.   Vol. 3 : Mezzo-Soprano.
    Vol. 4 : Contralto.   Vol. 5 : Tenor.   Vol. 6 : Baritone.   Vol. 7 : Bass.

IRELAND'S SONGS. A collection of 61 Standard and Popular Songs.

IRISH COUNTRY SONGS. Herbert Hughes. 4 Vols.

IRISH FOLK SONGS. 25 Songs, edited by Charles Wood.

IRISH MELODIES OF THOMAS MOORE, The. Op. 60. C. Villiers Stanford.

MANX NATIONAL SONGS. 51 Songs, edited by W. H. Gill (R.E.)

MOZART'S SONGS AND ARIAS. With German, Italian and English Words. Edited by J. Pittman and M. B. Foster (R.E.)

* **NATIONAL SONG BOOK.** Vol 2. 30 Old English Songs, edited by Harold Boulton and Arthur Somervell

* **NEW NATIONAL SONG BOOK.** Vol. I. 313 Folk Songs, Carols and Rounds, edited by C. Villiers Stanford, with revised piano accompaniments by the late Dr. J. Shaw.

OLD ENGLISH MELODIES. H. Lane Wilson. 21 Songs by Dr. Arne, Thomas Brown, Carey Dibdin, Hook, Leveridge, Smart, Young, etc.

OLD IRISH MELODIES. Herbert Hughes. 12 Songs.

PICK OF THE BUNCH. Eight Albums of Famous Songs.
    Vol. I : 7 Songs for Soprano.   Vol. 2 : 8 Songs for Tenor.
    Vol. 3 : 8 Songs for Mezzo-Soprano.   Vol. 4 : 8 Songs for Baritone.
    Vol 5 : 8 Songs for Contralto.   Vol. 6 : 6 Soldiers' Songs.
    Vol. 7 : 6 Sailors' Songs.   Vol. 8 : Seven Popular Humorous Songs for Baritone.

RUBINSTEIN'S SONGS. Fifty-nine Songs with German and English Words. (R.E.)

SAILORS' SONGS OR CHANTIES. Ferris Tozer. 50 Songs.

SELECT FRENCH SONGS FROM THE 12TH TO THE 18TH CENTURY. Arnold Dolmetsch.

SEVEN SEAS SHANTY BOOK, The. Taylor S. Harris. 42 Sea Shanties collected and recollected by John Sampson.

SONGS FROM MANY LANDS (Liedere van baie nasies). Helen V. S. Roberts. 24 Songs. English-Afrikaans.

SONGS FROM THE OPERAS. 50 Arias for Tenor and Baritone edited by J. Pittman (R.E.)

SONGS OF BRITAIN. Selected and edited by Frank Kidson and Martin Shaw. 100 English, Welsh, Scottish, and Irish Songs.

SONGS OF ENGLAND. 279 Songs edited by J. L. Hatton and E. Faning (R.E.) 3 Vols.

SONGS OF THE HEBRIDES. 156 Songs in 3 Vols. edited by Marjory and Patuffa Kennedy-Fraser. Also 3 Vols. of "Twelve Selected Songs of the Hebrides". For High or Low Voice

SONGS OF IRELAND. 87 Songs edited by J. L. Hatton and J. L. Molloy (R.E.)

SONGS OF ITALY. 54 Popular Italian Songs with Italian and English Words (R.E.)

SONGS OF OLD IRELAND. C. Villiers Stanford. 50 Old Irish Melodies.

SONGS OF SCANDINAVIA and Northern Europe. Edited by J. A. Kappey (R.E.) 84 Songs from Holland, Scandinavia, Finland, Russia and Poland.

SONGS OF SCOTLAND. 240 Songs edited by C. Brown, J. Pittman, M. B. Foster (R.E.). 2 Vols.

SONGS OF WALES. 70 Songs edited by Brinley Richards, English-Welsh (R.E.)

WELSH MELODIES. St. David's Edition. 32 Songs edited by J. Lloyd Williams and Arthur Somervell. With traditional and original Welsh words and English Lyrics by A. P. Graves. 2 Vols. (Vol. I for High or Low Voice. Vol. 2 for Low or Medium Voice only.)

* *Words and Melody Editions also available*

Abbreviation : (R.E.) Royal Edition.

For Prices see Current Catalogue.

Boosey & Hawkes, Ltd.

London · Paris · Bonn · Capetown · Sydney · Toronto · Buenos Aires · New York

No. 508

Vocal Albums

Boosey's Community Song Book*
English, Scottish, Welsh and Irish Songs

Club Song Book*
Separate editions for Boys and Girls
edited by Herbert Wiseman and Sydney Northcote

Elizabethan Love Songs
Two sets each of 30 Songs for High or Low Voice
arranged by Frederick Keel

Fifty Modern English Songs
Compositions by 20th Century Composers

Golden Treasury of Songs
Compositions by Classical Composers

Handel's Opera Songs
52 Arias edited by W. T. Best

Handel's Songs
Selected and edited by Walter Ford and R. Erlebach

Ireland's Songs
A Collection of 61 Standard and Popular Songs

Irish Country Songs
Edited and arranged in 4 volumes by Herbert Hughes

Irish Folk Songs
25 Songs edited by Charles Wood

Manx National Songs
51 Songs arranged by W. H. Gill

Mozart Songs and Arias
edited by J. Pittman and M. B. Foster

New National Song Book*
313 Folk Songs, Carols and Rounds
edited by C. Villiers Stanford

New Imperial Edition
A chronological anthology of Song
from the Lutenists down to the present day
Compiled, edited and arranged by Sydney Northcote
Separate editions for Bass, Baritone, Tenor,
Contralto, Mezzo-Soprano and Soprano

Old English Melodies
21 Songs edited by H. Lane Wilson

Old Irish Melodies
12 Songs edited by Herbert Hughes

Pick of the Bunch
Albums of Famous Songs
for Baritone, Tenor, Contralto, Mezzo-Soprano
and Soprano

Rubinstein's Songs
59 Songs with German and English words

Sailors' Songs or Chanties
50 Songs composed and arranged by Ferris Tozer

Select French Songs
From the 12th to the 18th Century
edited by A. Dolmetsch

Selected Songs
by Serge Rachmaninoff
Albums of 12 Songs for High or Medium Voice

Seven Seas Shanty Book
42 Sea Shanties edited by S. Taylor Harris

Songs from Many Lands
24 Songs in English and Africaan
edited by Helen V. S. Roberts

Songs of Britain
100 English, Scottish, Welsh and Irish Songs
Selected and edited by Frank Kidson and Martin Shaw

Songs of England
297 Songs edited by J. L. Hatton and E. Faning

Songs of the Hebrides
186 Songs in 3 volumes
Collected and arranged by M. and P. Kennedy-Fraser

Songs of Ireland
87 Songs edited by J. L. Hatton and J. L. Molloy

Songs of Italy
54 Popular Songs with Italian and English words

Songs of Old Ireland
50 Old Irish Melodies edited by C. Villiers Stanford

**Songs of Scandinavia
and Northern Europe**
84 Songs edited by J. A. Kappey

Songs of Scotland
*240 Songs edited in 2 volumes
by C. Brown, J. Pittman, M. B. Foster*

Songs of Wales
70 Songs edited by Brinley Richards

Twelve Selected Songs of the Hebrides
For High or Low Voice in 3 volumes
collected and arranged by M. and P. Kennedy-Fraser

Welsh Melodies
St. David's Edition of 32 Songs in 2 volumes
*by J. Lloyd-Williams and A. Somervell
Traditional and original Welsh words and English
lyrics by A. P. Graves*

Youth's Golden Treasury of Song*
Compositions by well-known Composers

***Words and Melody Editions also published**

Boosey & Hawkes

Limited
295 Regent Street, London, W.1

Paris · Bonn · Capetown · Sydney · Toronto · Buenos Aires · New York

...us Celinda. I'll sail upon the Dog-Star.

...*separately*). There is not a swain in the

...Thou tunest this world. 'Tis holiday.

Piano
nd Piano
Piano

er Ford
Erlebach

...*lia*). Author of peace (*Saul*). Straight ...no, I'll take no less (*Seville*). O lovely ...ands (*Solomon*).

...*nthem*). O King of Kings (*Esther*). In ...ctuating state (*Belshazzar*). Prophetic ...*Choice of Hercules*).

...*ler Balus*). What means this weight ? ...(*Time and Truth*).

VOLUME IV : CONTRALTO

Pleasure's gentle zephyrs (*Time and Truth*). Guards, seize the traitor (*Esther*). Impious mortal (*Deborah*). Then long eternity (*Samson*). She weeps (*Semele*). Great God (*Belshazzar*). See with what sad dejection (*Hercules*). Gold now is common (*Solomon*). Frost nips the flowers (*Susanna*). O bright example (*Theodora*). Yet can I hear (*The Choice of Hercules*).

VOLUME V : TENOR

Beatus vir (*Nisi Dominus*). Though bound (*Second Passion*). God is a constant sure defence (*Chandos Anthem*). Who dares (*Esther*). Would you gain (*Acis and Galatea*). The mighty master (*Alexander's Feast*). Great Dagon (*Samson*). Let the deep bowl (*Belshazzar*). Despair not (*Hercules*). O Lord, how many are my foes (*Occasional Oratorio*). To God who made the radiant sun (*Alexander Balus*). So long the memory (*Joshua*). From morn to eve (*Solomon*). Blessed are they (*Foundling Hospital Anthem*). Enjoy the sweet Elysian grove (*Alcesto*). Horror ! Confusion ! (*Jephta*). Pensive sorrow (*Time and Truth*).

VOLUME VI : BARITONE

O work sublime (*First Passion*). Ha ! What vision (*La Resurrezione*). That God is great (*Chandos Anthem*). Turn not (*Esther*). Mountains on whose barren breast (*L'Allegro*). O Memory (*Belshazzar*). Oh Jove ! (*Hercules*). To God our strength (*Occasional Oratorio*). And thus let happy Egypt's king (*Alexander Balus*). 'Tis Diocletian's natal day (*Theodora*). Ye fleeting shades (*Alceste*). Let me congratulate (*Jephta*). You hoped to call in vain (*Time and Truth*).

VOLUME VII : BASS

Ye heavens (*Second Passion*). O praise the Lord (*Chandos Anthem*). When storms the proud (*Athalia*). A serpent in my bosom (*Saul*). Vouchsafe, o Lord (*Dettingen Te Deum*). Since the race of time (*Joseph*). Leave me (*Semele*). Alcides' name (*Hercules*). To power immortal (*Belshazzar*). Why do the gentiles tumult (*Occasional Oratorio*). Great Prince (*Solomon*). Peace crowned (*Susanna*). Wide spread his name (*Theodora*). Like the shadow (*Time and Truth*).

The above-mentioned titles are not comprehensive to each volume.
For the complete contents consult the catalogue of Albums, Song Cycles, etc.

Boosey & Hawkes
Limited
295 Regent Street, London, W.1
Paris · Bonn · Capetown · Sydney · Toronto · Buenos Aires · New York

No. 602

6.51